To:

_____

From:

_____

Date:

_____

The Lᴏʀᴅ is my shepherd, I shall not be in want.

~ Psalm 23:1

In all things God works for the good of those who love Him,
who have been called according to His purpose.

~ Romans 8:28

You have made known to me the path of life; You will fill me with
joy in Your presence, with eternal pleasures at Your right hand.

~ Psalm 16:11

As for God, His way is perfect; the word of the LORD is flawless.
He is a shield for all who take refuge in Him.

~ 2 Samuel 22:31

Ascribe to the LORD the glory due His name. Bring an offering and come before Him; worship the LORD in the splendor of His holiness.

~ 1 Chronicles 16:29

Shout for joy to the LORD, burst into jubilant song with music.

~ Psalm 98:4

The eternal God is your refuge, and underneath are the everlasting arms.

~ Deuteronomy 33:27

_____

_____

_____

_____

_____

_____

_____

_____

_____

_____

_____

_____

_____

_____

_____

_____

_____

_____

_____

_____

_____

_____

_____

_____

_____

"Be strong and courageous. Do not be terrified; for the Lord
your God will be with you wherever you go."

~ Joshua 1:9

He will yet fill your mouth with laughter and your lips with shouts of joy.

~ Job 8:21

O LORD, our Lord, how majestic is Your name in all the earth!

~ Psalm 8:9

The Lord will watch over your coming and going both now and forevermore.
~ Psalm 121:8

The heavens declare the glory of God; the skies proclaim the work of His hands.

~ Psalm 19:1

The LORD is my light and my salvation – whom shall I fear?
The LORD is the stronghold of my life – of whom shall I be afraid?
~ Psalm 27:1

_____

_____

_____

_____

_____

_____

_____

_____

_____

_____

_____

_____

_____

_____

_____

_____

_____

_____

_____

_____

_____

_____

One thing I ask of the LORD, this is what I seek:
that I may dwell in the house of the LORD all the days of my life.

~ Psalm 27:4

Taste and see that the LORD is good; blessed is the man who takes refuge in Him.

~ Psalm 34:8

God has made everything beautiful in its time.

~ Ecclesiastes 3:11

Praise be to the God and Father of our Lord Jesus Christ,
who has blessed us with every spiritual blessing in Christ.

My help comes from the LORD, the Maker of heaven and earth.

~Psalm 121:2

Finally, be strong in the Lord and in His mighty power.

~ Ephesians 6:10

_____

_____

_____

_____

_____

_____

_____

_____

_____

_____

_____

_____

_____

_____

_____

_____

_____

_____

_____

_____

_____

Rejoice in the Lord always. I will say it again: Rejoice!
~ Philippians 4:4

Faith is being sure of what we hope for and certain of what we do not see.

~ Hebrews 11:1

_____

_____

_____

_____

_____

_____

_____

_____

_____

_____

_____

_____

_____

_____

_____

_____

_____

_____

_____

_____

_____

"Do not let your hearts be troubled. Trust in God; trust also in Me."

~ John 14:1

"Let your light shine before men, that they may see
your good deeds and praise your Father in heaven."
~ Matthew 5:16

"Blessed are those who hunger and thirst for righteousness, for they will be filled."
~ Matthew 5:6

"But seek first His kingdom and His righteousness,
and all these things will be given to you as well."
~ Matthew 6:33

"Ask and it will be given to you; seek and you will find;
knock and the door will be opened to you."
~ Matthew 7:7

From the fullness of His grace we have all received one blessing after another.

~ John 1:16

Shout for joy to the LORD, all the earth.

~ Psalm 100:1

Come, let us sing for joy to the LORD; let us shout aloud to the Rock of our salvation.
~ Psalm 95:1

How many are Your works, O LORD! In wisdom You made them all;
the earth is full of Your creatures.

~ Psalm 104:24

The fear of the Lord is the beginning of wisdom;
all who follow His precepts have good understanding.

~ Psalm 111:10

You will keep in perfect peace him whose mind is steadfast, because he trusts in You.
~ Isaiah 26:3

The Lord is my shepherd, I shall not be in want.

~ Psalm 23:1

In all things God works for the good of those who love Him,
who have been called according to His purpose.

~ Romans 8:28

The eternal God is your refuge, and underneath are the everlasting arms.

~ Deuteronomy 33:27

"Be strong and courageous. Do not be terrified; for the LORD
your God will be with you wherever you go."

~ Joshua 1:9

You have made known to me the path of life; You will fill me with
joy in Your presence, with eternal pleasures at Your right hand.

~ Psalm 16:11

As for God, His way is perfect; the word of the LORD is flawless.
He is a shield for all who take refuge in Him.

~ 2 Samuel 22:31

Ascribe to the LORD the glory due His name. Bring an offering and come before Him; worship the LORD in the splendor of His holiness.

~ 1 Chronicles 16:29

Shout for joy to the Lord, burst into jubilant song with music.

~ Psalm 98:4

He will yet fill your mouth with laughter and your lips with shouts of joy.

~ Job 8:21

O LORD, our Lord, how majestic is Your name in all the earth!

~ Psalm 8:9

The Lord will watch over your coming and going both now and forevermore.
~ Psalm 121:8

The heavens declare the glory of God; the skies proclaim the work of His hands.

~ Psalm 19:1

The LORD is my light and my salvation – whom shall I fear?
The LORD is the stronghold of my life – of whom shall I be afraid?
~ Psalm 27:1

One thing I ask of the LORD, this is what I seek:
that I may dwell in the house of the LORD all the days of my life.

~ Psalm 27:4

Taste and see that the LORD is good; blessed is the man who takes refuge in Him.

~ Psalm 34:8

God has made everything beautiful in its time.

~ Ecclesiastes 3:11

Praise be to the God and Father of our Lord Jesus Christ,
who has blessed us with every spiritual blessing in Christ.

~ Ephesians 1:3

My help comes from the LORD, the Maker of heaven and earth.
~Psalm 121:2

Finally, be strong in the Lord and in His mighty power.

~ Ephesians 6:10

Rejoice in the Lord always. I will say it again: Rejoice!
~ Philippians 4:4

Faith is being sure of what we hope for and certain of what we do not see.

~ Hebrews 11:1

"Do not let your hearts be troubled. Trust in God; trust also in Me."

~ John 14:1

"Let your light shine before men, that they may see
your good deeds and praise your Father in heaven."
~ Matthew 5:16

"Blessed are those who hunger and thirst for righteousness, for they will be filled."
~ Matthew 5:6

"But seek first His kingdom and His righteousness,
and all these things will be given to you as well."
~ Matthew 6:33

"Ask and it will be given to you; seek and you will find;
knock and the door will be opened to you."

~ Matthew 7:7

From the fullness of His grace we have all received one blessing after another.

~ John 1:16

Shout for joy to the LORD, all the earth.

~ Psalm 100:1

Come, let us sing for joy to the LORD; let us shout aloud to the Rock of our salvation.

~ Psalm 95:1

How many are Your works, O Lord! In wisdom You made them all;
the earth is full of Your creatures.

~ Psalm 104:24

The fear of the LORD is the beginning of wisdom;
all who follow His precepts have good understanding.

~ Psalm 111:10

You will keep in perfect peace him whose mind is steadfast, because he trusts in You.

~ Isaiah 26:3

The Lord is my shepherd, I shall not be in want.

~ Psalm 23:1

In all things God works for the good of those who love Him,
who have been called according to His purpose.

~ Romans 8:28

The eternal God is your refuge, and underneath are the everlasting arms.
~ Deuteronomy 33:27

_____

_____

_____

_____

_____

_____

_____

_____

_____

_____

_____

_____

_____

_____

_____

_____

_____

_____

_____

_____

_____

_____

_____

"Be strong and courageous. Do not be terrified; for the LORD
your God will be with you wherever you go."

~ Joshua 1:9

You have made known to me the path of life; You will fill me with
joy in Your presence, with eternal pleasures at Your right hand.

~ Psalm 16:11

As for God, His way is perfect; the word of the LORD is flawless.
He is a shield for all who take refuge in Him.

~ 2 Samuel 22:31

Ascribe to the LORD the glory due His name. Bring an offering and come before Him; worship the LORD in the splendor of His holiness.

~ 1 Chronicles 16:29

Shout for joy to the LORD, burst into jubilant song with music.

~ Psalm 98:4

He will yet fill your mouth with laughter and your lips with shouts of joy.

~ Job 8:21

O LORD, our Lord, how majestic is Your name in all the earth!

~ Psalm 8:9

The Lord will watch over your coming and going both now and forevermore.

~ Psalm 121:8

The heavens declare the glory of God; the skies proclaim the work of His hands.

~ Psalm 19:1

The LORD is my light and my salvation – whom shall I fear?
The LORD is the stronghold of my life – of whom shall I be afraid?

~ Psalm 27:1

One thing I ask of the LORD, this is what I seek:
that I may dwell in the house of the LORD all the days of my life.

~ Psalm 27:4

Taste and see that the LORD is good; blessed is the man who takes refuge in Him.
~ Psalm 34:8

God has made everything beautiful in its time.

~ Ecclesiastes 3:11

Praise be to the God and Father of our Lord Jesus Christ,
who has blessed us with every spiritual blessing in Christ.

~ Ephesians 1:3

My help comes from the LORD, the Maker of heaven and earth.

~Psalm 121:2

Finally, be strong in the Lord and in His mighty power.

~ Ephesians 6:10

Rejoice in the Lord always. I will say it again: Rejoice!

~ Philippians 4:4

Faith is being sure of what we hope for and certain of what we do not see.
~ Hebrews 11:1

"Do not let your hearts be troubled. Trust in God; trust also in Me."

~ John 14:1

"Let your light shine before men, that they may see
your good deeds and praise your Father in heaven."
~ Matthew 5:16

"Blessed are those who hunger and thirst for righteousness, for they will be filled."
~ Matthew 5:6

"But seek first His kingdom and His righteousness,
and all these things will be given to you as well."

~ Matthew 6:33

_____

_____

_____

_____

_____

_____

_____

_____

_____

_____

_____

_____

_____

_____

_____

_____

_____

_____

_____

_____

_____

_____

_____

_____

_____

"Ask and it will be given to you; seek and you will find;
knock and the door will be opened to you."

~ Matthew 7:7

From the fullness of His grace we have all received one blessing after another.

~ John 1:16

Shout for joy to the LORD, all the earth.

~ Psalm 100:1

Come, let us sing for joy to the LORD; let us shout aloud to the Rock of our salvation.

~ Psalm 95:1

How many are Your works, O Lord! In wisdom You made them all;
the earth is full of Your creatures.

~ Psalm 104:24

The fear of the LORD is the beginning of wisdom;
all who follow His precepts have good understanding.

You will keep in perfect peace him whose mind is steadfast, because he trusts in You.
~ Isaiah 26:3

The LORD is my shepherd, I shall not be in want.

~ Psalm 23:1

In all things God works for the good of those who love Him,
who have been called according to His purpose.

~ Romans 8:28

The eternal God is your refuge, and underneath are the everlasting arms.
~ Deuteronomy 33:27

_____

_____

_____

_____

_____

_____

_____

_____

_____

_____

_____

_____

_____

_____

_____

_____

_____

_____

_____

_____

_____

_____

_____

"Be strong and courageous. Do not be terrified; for the LORD
your God will be with you wherever you go."

~ Joshua 1:9

You have made known to me the path of life; You will fill me with
joy in Your presence, with eternal pleasures at Your right hand.

~ Psalm 16:11

As for God, His way is perfect; the word of the LORD is flawless.
He is a shield for all who take refuge in Him.

~ 2 Samuel 22:31

Ascribe to the LORD the glory due His name. Bring an offering and come before Him;
worship the LORD in the splendor of His holiness.

~ 1 Chronicles 16:29

Shout for joy to the LORD, burst into jubilant song with music.

~ Psalm 98:4

He will yet fill your mouth with laughter and your lips with shouts of joy.

~ Job 8:21

O Lord, our Lord, how majestic is Your name in all the earth!

~ Psalm 8:9

The Lord will watch over your coming and going both now and forevermore.
~ Psalm 121:8

The heavens declare the glory of God; the skies proclaim the work of His hands.

~ Psalm 19:1

The LORD is my light and my salvation – whom shall I fear?
The LORD is the stronghold of my life – of whom shall I be afraid?

~ Psalm 27:1

One thing I ask of the LORD, this is what I seek:
that I may dwell in the house of the LORD all the days of my life.

~ Psalm 27:4

Taste and see that the LORD is good; blessed is the man who takes refuge in Him.

~ Psalm 34:8

God has made everything beautiful in its time.

~ Ecclesiastes 3:11

Praise be to the God and Father of our Lord Jesus Christ,
who has blessed us with every spiritual blessing in Christ.

~ Ephesians 1:3

My help comes from the LORD, the Maker of heaven and earth.

~Psalm 121:2

Finally, be strong in the Lord and in His mighty power.

~ Ephesians 6:10

Rejoice in the Lord always. I will say it again: Rejoice!

~ Philippians 4:4

Faith is being sure of what we hope for and certain of what we do not see.

~ Hebrews 11:1

"Do not let your hearts be troubled. Trust in God; trust also in Me."

~ John 14:1

"Let your light shine before men, that they may see
your good deeds and praise your Father in heaven."
~ Matthew 5:16

_____

_____

_____

_____

_____

_____

_____

_____

_____

_____

_____

_____

_____

_____

_____

_____

_____

_____

_____

_____

_____

_____

_____

_____

"Blessed are those who hunger and thirst for righteousness, for they will be filled."

~ Matthew 5:6

"But seek first His kingdom and His righteousness,
and all these things will be given to you as well."
~ Matthew 6:33

"Ask and it will be given to you; seek and you will find;
knock and the door will be opened to you."

~ Matthew 7:7

From the fullness of His grace we have all received one blessing after another.

~ John 1:16

Shout for joy to the LORD, all the earth.

~ Psalm 100:1

Come, let us sing for joy to the LORD; let us shout aloud to the Rock of our salvation.
~ Psalm 95:1

How many are Your works, O Lord! In wisdom You made them all;
the earth is full of Your creatures.

~ Psalm 104:24

The fear of the LORD is the beginning of wisdom;
all who follow His precepts have good understanding.

~ Psalm 111:10

You will keep in perfect peace him whose mind is steadfast, because he trusts in You.

~ Isaiah 26:3

The LORD is my shepherd, I shall not be in want.

~ Psalm 23:1

In all things God works for the good of those who love Him,
who have been called according to His purpose.

~ Romans 8:28

The eternal God is your refuge, and underneath are the everlasting arms.

~ Deuteronomy 33:27

"Be strong and courageous. Do not be terrified; for the Lord your God will be with you wherever you go."
~ Joshua 1:9

You have made known to me the path of life; You will fill me with
joy in Your presence, with eternal pleasures at Your right hand.

~ Psalm 16:11

As for God, His way is perfect; the word of the LORD is flawless.
He is a shield for all who take refuge in Him.

~ 2 Samuel 22:31

Ascribe to the LORD the glory due His name. Bring an offering and come before Him; worship the LORD in the splendor of His holiness.

~ 1 Chronicles 16:29

Shout for joy to the LORD, burst into jubilant song with music.

~ Psalm 98:4

He will yet fill your mouth with laughter and your lips with shouts of joy.

~ Job 8:21

O Lord, our Lord, how majestic is Your name in all the earth!

~ Psalm 8:9

The LORD will watch over your coming and going both now and forevermore.
~ Psalm 121:8

The heavens declare the glory of God; the skies proclaim the work of His hands.

~ Psalm 19:1

The LORD is my light and my salvation – whom shall I fear?
The LORD is the stronghold of my life – of whom shall I be afraid?

~ Psalm 27:1

One thing I ask of the Lord, this is what I seek:
that I may dwell in the house of the Lord all the days of my life.

~ Psalm 27:4

Taste and see that the LORD is good; blessed is the man who takes refuge in Him.

~ Psalm 34:8

God has made everything beautiful in its time.

~ Ecclesiastes 3:11

Praise be to the God and Father of our Lord Jesus Christ,
who has blessed us with every spiritual blessing in Christ.

~ Ephesians 1:3

My help comes from the LORD, the Maker of heaven and earth.
~Psalm 121:2

Finally, be strong in the Lord and in His mighty power.

~ Ephesians 6:10

Rejoice in the Lord always. I will say it again: Rejoice!

~ Philippians 4:4

Faith is being sure of what we hope for and certain of what we do not see.
~ Hebrews 11:1

_____

_____

_____

_____

_____

_____

_____

_____

_____

_____

_____

_____

_____

_____

_____

_____

_____

_____

_____

_____

_____

_____

_____

_____

"Do not let your hearts be troubled. Trust in God; trust also in Me."

~ John 14:1

"Let your light shine before men, that they may see
your good deeds and praise your Father in heaven."
~ Matthew 5:16

"Blessed are those who hunger and thirst for righteousness, for they will be filled."
~ Matthew 5:6

"But seek first His kingdom and His righteousness,
and all these things will be given to you as well."
~ Matthew 6:33

"Ask and it will be given to you; seek and you will find;
knock and the door will be opened to you."

~ Matthew 7:7

From the fullness of His grace we have all received one blessing after another.

~ John 1:16

Shout for joy to the LORD, all the earth.

~ Psalm 100:1

Come, let us sing for joy to the LORD; let us shout aloud to the Rock of our salvation.
~ Psalm 95:1

How many are Your works, O Lord! In wisdom You made them all;
the earth is full of Your creatures.

~ Psalm 104:24